DesignOriginals

Creative Coloring Animals

Valentina Harper

an Imprint of Fox Chapel Publishing
www.d-originals.com

Basic Color Ideas

In order to truly enjoy this coloring book, you must remember that there is no wrong way—or right way—to paint or use color. My drawings are created precisely so that you can enjoy the process no matter what method you choose to use to color them!

The most important thing to keep in mind is that each illustration was made to be enjoyed as you are coloring, to give you a period of relaxation and fun at the same time. Each picture is filled with details and forms that you can choose to color in many different ways. I value each person's individual creative process, so I want you to play and have fun with all of your favorite color combinations.

As you color, you can look at each illustration as a whole, or you can color each part as a separate piece that, when brought together, makes the image complete. That is why it is up to you to choose your own process, take your time, and, above all, enjoy your own way of doing things.

To the right are a few examples of ways that you can color each drawing.

Color each section of the drawing (every general area, not every tiny shape) in one single color.

Within each section, color each detail (small shape) in alternating colors.

Leave some areas white to add a sense of space and lightness to the illustration.

Basic Color Tips

As an artist, I love to mix techniques, colors, and different mediums when it comes time to add color to my works of art. And when it comes to colors, the brighter the better! I feel that with color, illustrations take on a life of their own.

Remember: when it comes to painting and coloring, there are no rules. The most fun part is to play with color, relax, and enjoy the process and the beautiful finished result.

Feel free to mix and match colors and tones. Work your way from primary colors to secondary colors to tertiary colors, combining different tones to create all kinds of different effects. If you aren't familiar with color theory, below is a quick, easy guide to the basic colors and combinations you will be able to create.

Primary colors: These are the colors that cannot be obtained by mixing any other colors; they are yellow, blue, and red.

Secondary colors: These colors are obtained by mixing two primary colors in equal parts; they are green, purple, and orange.

Tertiary colors: These colors are obtained by mixing one primary color and one secondary color.

Don't be afraid of mixing colors and creating your own palettes. Play with colors—the possibilities are endless!

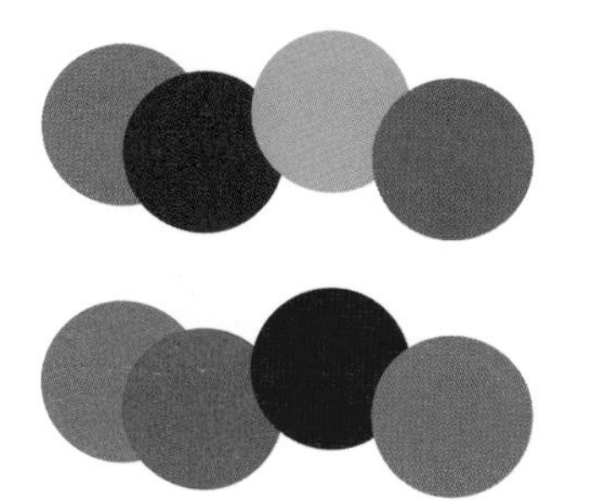

Color Inspiration

On the following eight pages, you'll see fully colored samples of my illustrations in this book, as interpreted by one talented artist and author, Marie Browning. I was delighted to invite Marie to color my work, and she used many different mediums to do so, all listed below each image. Take a look at how Marie decided to color the doodles, and find some inspiration for your own coloring! After the colored samples, the thirty delightful drawings just waiting for your color begin. Remember the tips I showed you earlier, think of the color inspiration you've seen, and choose your favorite medium to get started, whether it's pencil, marker, watercolor, or something else. Your time to color begins now, and only ends when you run out of pages! Have fun!

Valentina Harper

Watercolors (Winsor & Newton), Irojiten Colored Pencils (Tombow). Tropical Tones. Color by Marie Browning.

Dual Brush Markers (Tombow). Bright Tones.
Color by Marie Browning.

Dual Brush Markers (Tombow), Gel Pens (Sakura).
Bright Tones. Color by Marie Browning.

Watercolors (Winsor & Newton).
Deep, Natural Tones. Color by Marie Browning.

Pitt Pastel Pencils (Faber-Castel), White Gel Pens (Sakura).
Sea Tones. Color by Marie Browning.

Irojiten Colored Pencils (Tombow). Muted Tones, Fluorescent eyes. Color by Marie Browning.

Dual Brush Markers (Tombow), Irojiten Colored Pencils (Tombow). Vivid Tones. Color by Marie Browning.

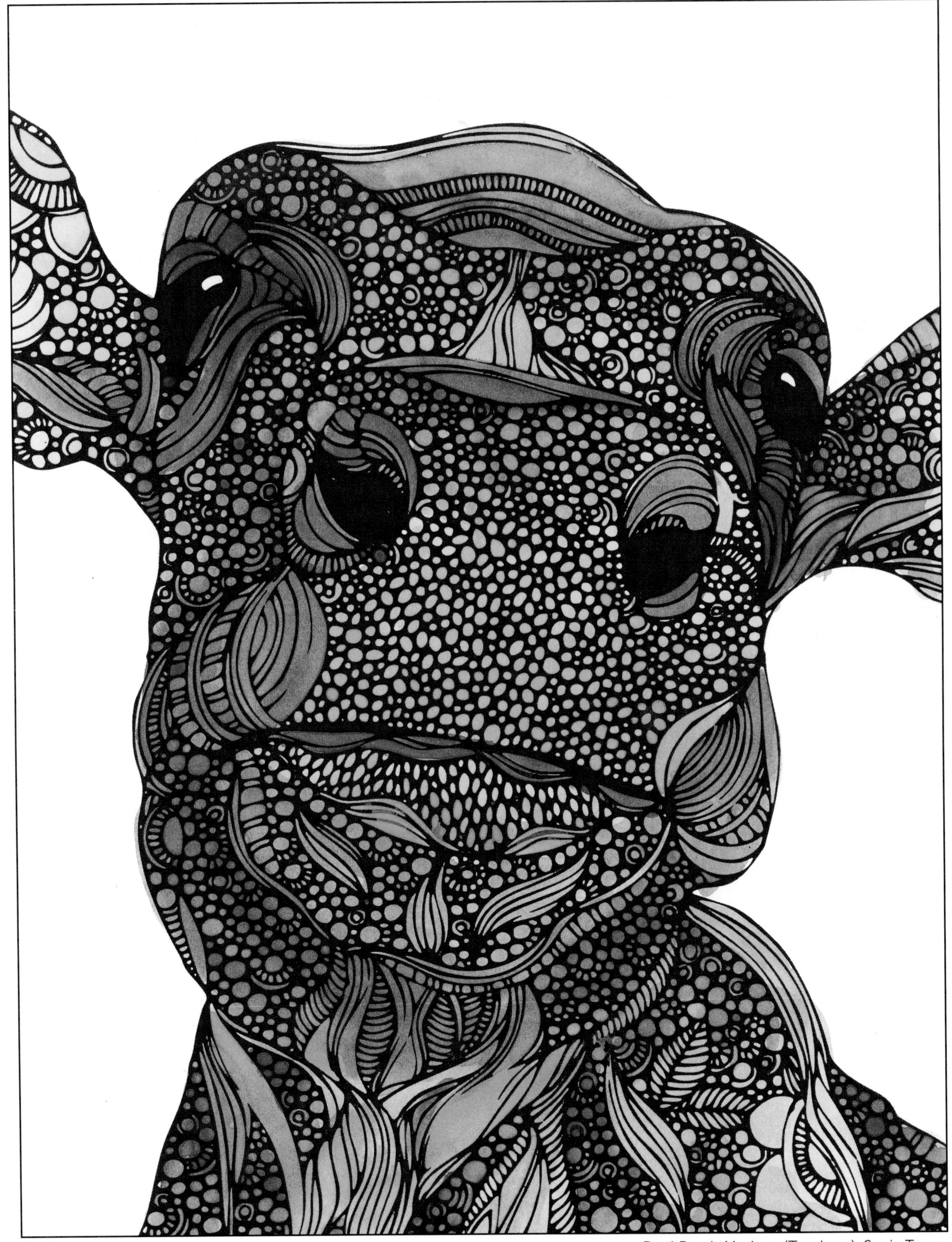

Dual Brush Markers (Tombow). Sepia Tones.
Color by Marie Browning.

Knowledge is knowing what to say.
Wisdom is knowing when to say it.

—Unknown

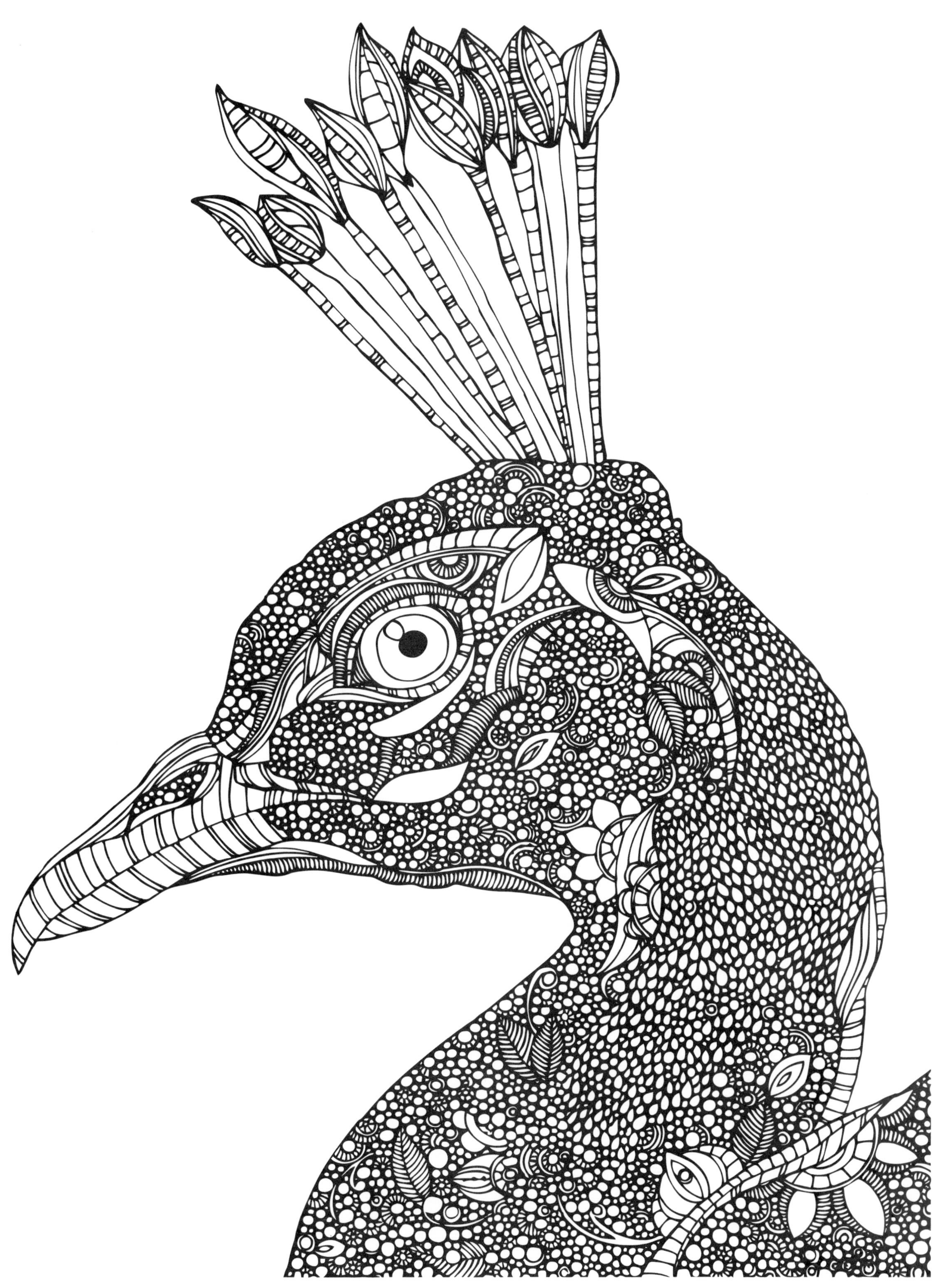

Why fit in, when you were
born to stand out?

—Mia Hamm

Alexis

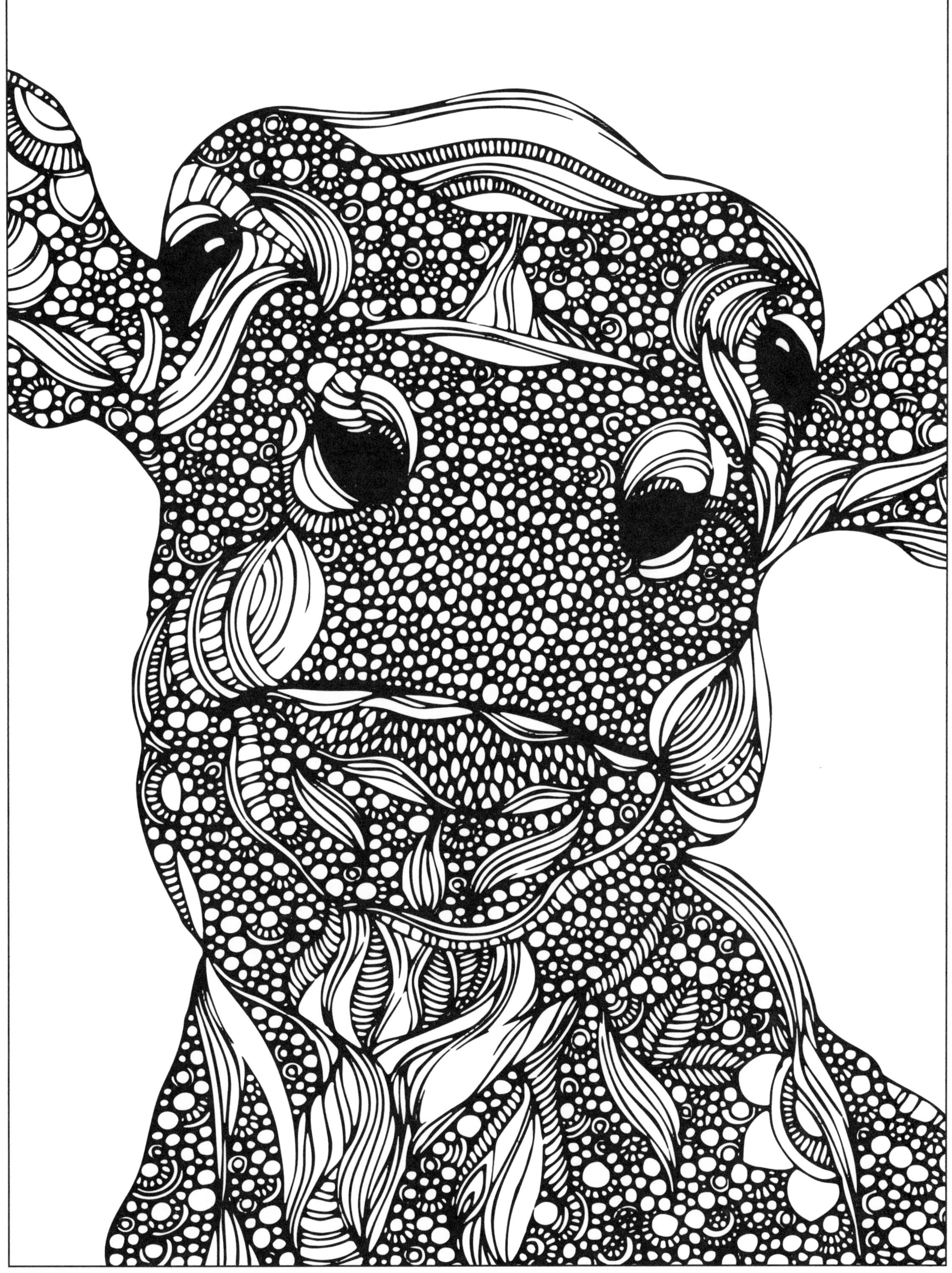

Until one has loved an animal, a part of one's soul remains unawakened.

—Anatole France

Arabella

If I could be half the person my dog is,
I'd be twice the human I am.

—Charles Yu

Barkisimeto

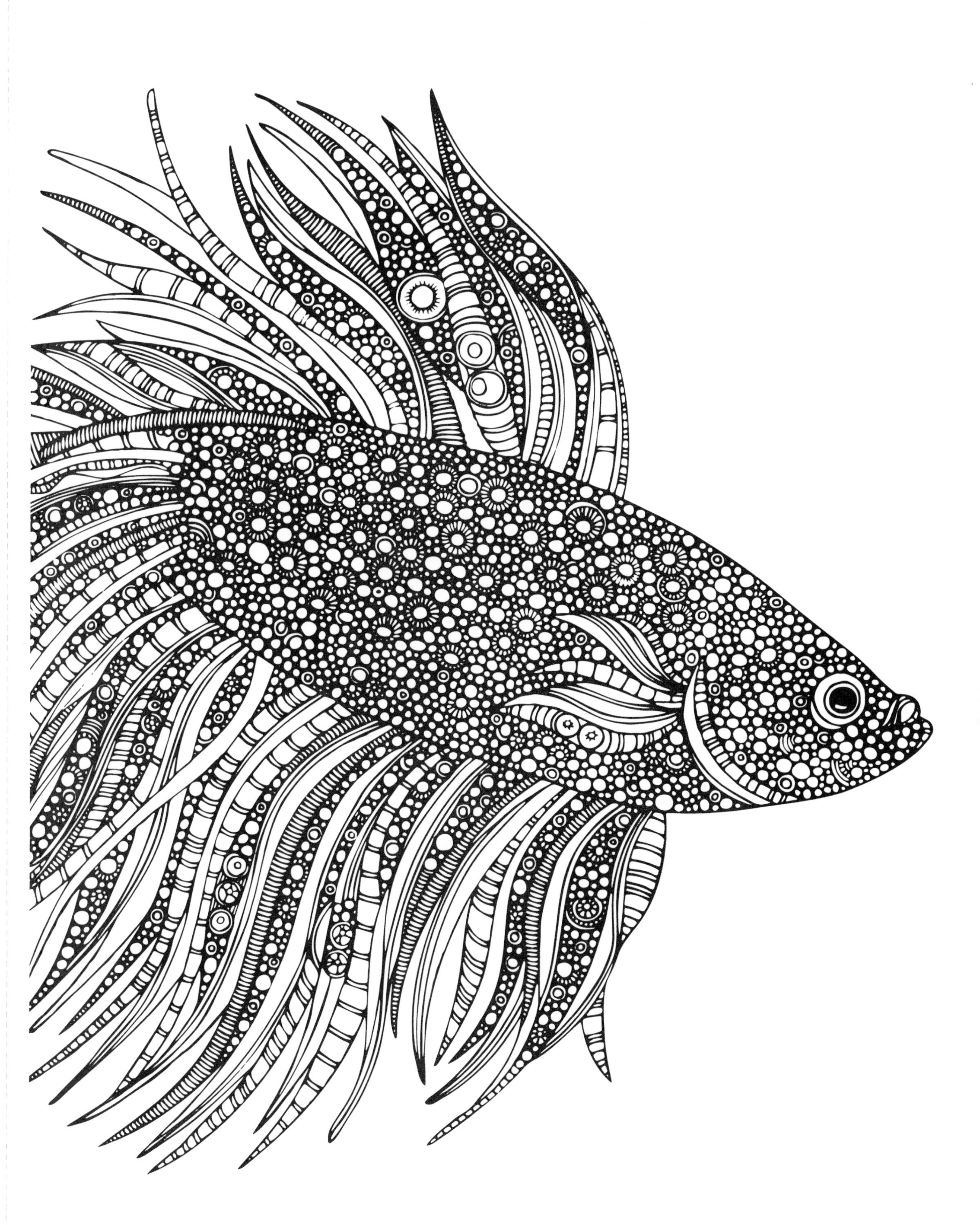

Smell the sea and feel the sky, let your soul and spirit fly into the mystic.

—Van Morrison

Beta Fish

Trust yourself, you know
more than you think you do.

—Benjamin Spock

The Deer

You can never cross the ocean unless you have the courage to lose sight of the shore.

—Unknown

Be happy for this moment.
This moment is your life.

—Omar Khayyam

I've decided to be happy,
because it is good for my health.

—Voltaire

The world needs dreamers and the world needs doers. But above all, the world needs dreamers who do.

—Sarah Ban Breathnach

Choose a job you love, and you will never have to work a day in your life.

—Unknown

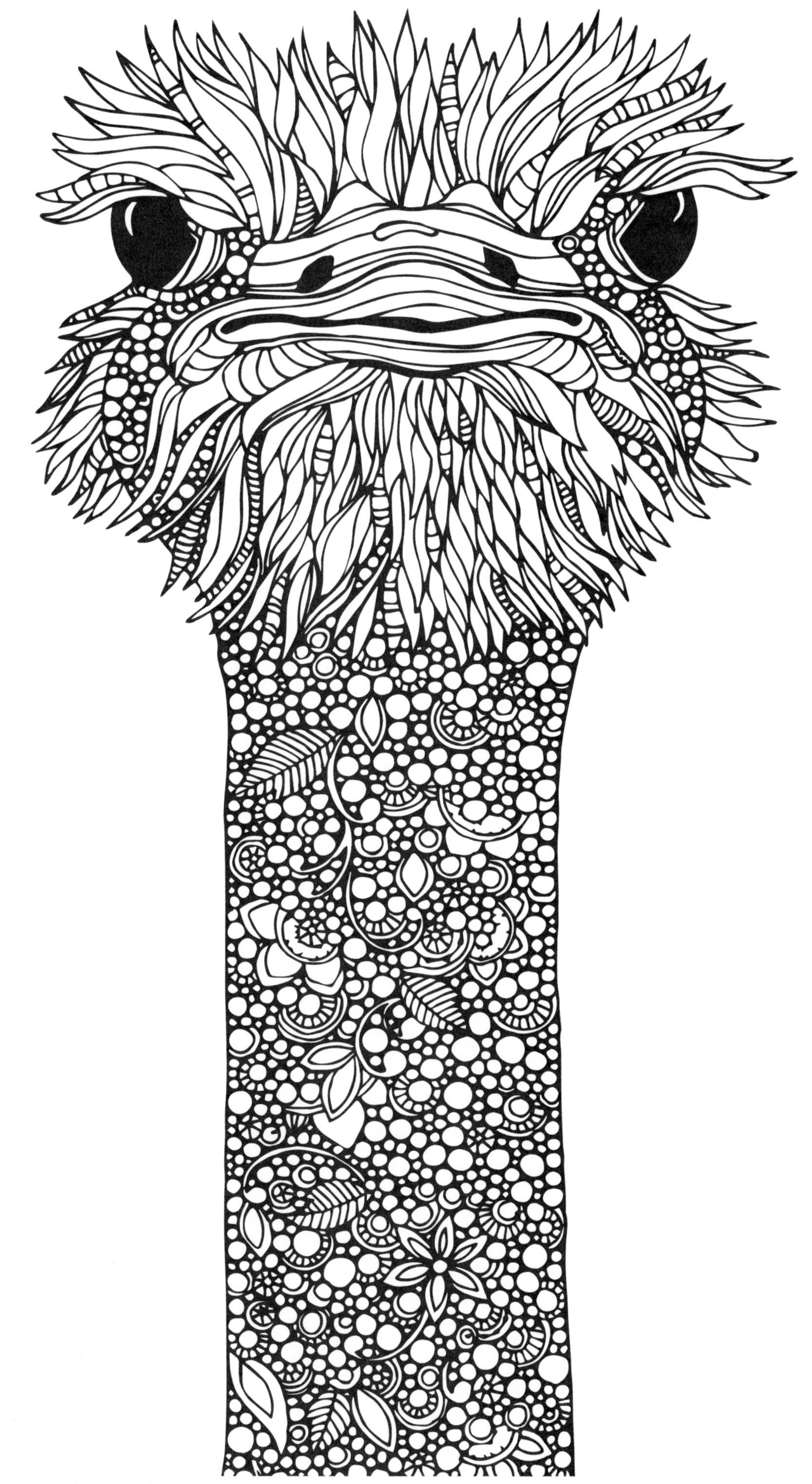

Be proud of who you are
rather than what you have.

—Unknown

Strength does not
come from physical capacity.
It comes from an indomitable will.

—Mahatma Gandhi

Dream higher than the sky
and deeper than the ocean.

—Unknown

Love comforteth like sunshine after rain.

—William Shakespeare

Out of your vulnerabilities
will come your strength.

—Sigmund Freud

Never get so busy making a living
that you forget to make a life.

—Unknown

We do not stop playing because we grow old,
we grow old because we stop playing.

—Unknown

Pinky

Not all those who wander are lost.

—J.R.R. Tolkien

Paul

There are two gifts we
should give our children:
one is roots, and the other is wings.

—Unknown

Success is the sum of small efforts,
repeated day in and day out.

—Robert Collier

I can be changed by what happens to me.
But I refuse to be reduced by it.

—Maya Angelou

It takes courage to grow up and
turn out to be who you really are.

—e.e. cummings

The sea, once it casts its spell,
holds one in its net of wonder forever.

—Jacques Cousteau

Octopus Bloom

Those who dwell among the
beauties and mysteries of the earth
are never alone or weary of life.

—Rachel Carson

Hope is the thing with feathers
That perches in the soul
And sings the tune without the words
And never stops at all.

—Emily Dickinson

Frisky Christy

I am only one, but I am one.
I cannot do everything,
but I can do something.
And because I cannot do everything,
I will not refuse to do the
something that I can do.

—Edward Everett Hale

Deer and Flowers

Just when the caterpillar thought its world was over, it became a butterfly.

—Unknown

It's not about how you look,
it's about how you see!

—Unknown

Phileus Frog

If you are not willing to learn,
no one can help you.
If you are determined to learn,
no one can stop you.

—Unknown